Eisenhower School

DISCARD

D1129508

WORLD OF ADVENTURE SERIES

The Lost Uranium Mine

Hunting Grizzly Bears

Fire on the Mountain

City Beneath the Sea

The Search for Piranha

Sacred Well of Sacrifice

THE SEARCH
FOR PIRANHA

By
Henry Bamman
Robert Whitehead

Illustrations
Darrell Wiskur

BENEFIC PRESS • CHICAGO

Publishing Division of Beckley-Cardy Company

Atlanta   Dallas   Long Beach   Portland

WHY?   WHAT?   WHERE?

Mark and Rich fly to Brazil in search of a live piranha for an aquarium. Their search takes them far
up the Amazon River to a small Indian village, where
they see a school of the deadly piranha in action.

Library of Congress
Number 64-14312

Copyright 1974, 1964 by Benefic Press
All Rights Reserved
Printed in the United States of America

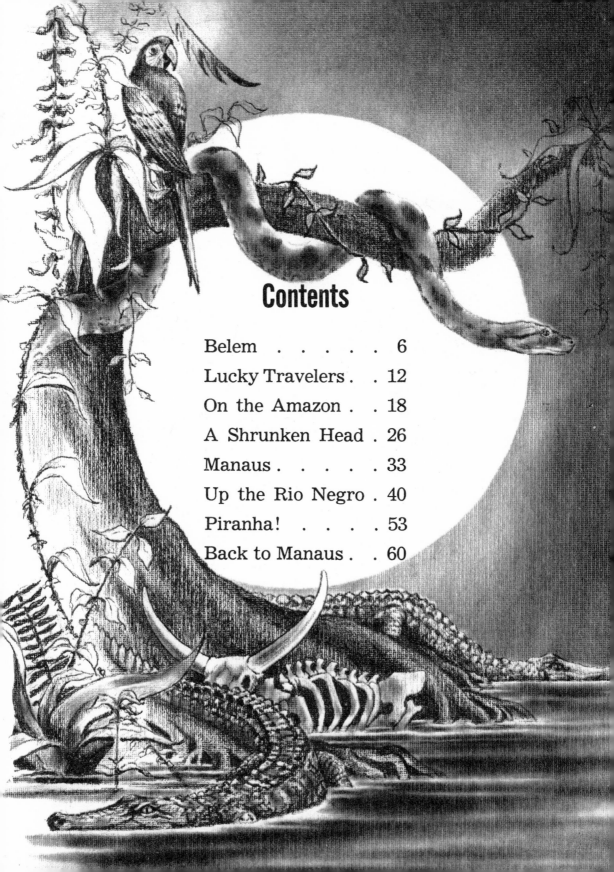

Contents

Belem

"It looks just like a fuzzy carpet!" said Rich, as he leaned over Mark's shoulder and looked out of the window of the airplane at the green jungle that was far below. "Wouldn't you hate to get lost in that?"

A man seated across from the two young men smiled and leaned toward them. "Many people have been lost in that jungle, but very few of them have come out alive. As you can see, there are no towns or cities in the jungle. It is known as one of the worst jungles in the world."

Mark and Rich watched the green of the jungle as the airplane flew on and on. Suddenly, Mark exclaimed, "There it is! There's the Amazon!"

Like a great brown snake, a mighty river wound through the jungle below. The pilot turned the plane, and then they were following the river. The men watched miles and miles of the twisting river pass beneath them. Suddenly, the plane turned sharply, and the pilot said, "Please fasten your seat belts. We are landing in Belem."

Mark pointed out of the window on their side of the airplane. As far as the men could see, there was water and jungle. The Amazon had divided into more than a dozen rivers.

"That's the mouth of the Amazon," said Mark. "I guess I should say those are the mouths, because the Amazon has more than a dozen mouths."

The airplane dropped lower and lower. The jungle seemed thicker and the water looked browner than they had from further up.

"There's Belem," said the man across from them.

As the airplane turned once more, a great city began to spread out before the young men. "Wow!" said Mark. "That is a big city!" Just then they saw the river again. There were hundreds of ships and boats on the river and at the docks.

"Look at the red sails on those boats," said Rich. "And just look at the ships!"

The man across from them smiled again. "Belem is one of the busiest ports in Brazil," he said. "From there, ships can go up the Amazon for nearly two thousand miles. No other river in the world can carry big ships that far. Are you fellows planning on going up the river?"

"Yes, we are. That is, if we can find a ship to take us," Mark replied.

There was a sudden jolt as the wheels of the plane touched the runway. Buildings, trees, and people flashed by as the plane moved along the runway. It was suddenly very hot. The plane came to a stop, and the pilot said, "Please stay in your seats. I'm sorry, but we will have to wait until the rain stops."

"What rain?" asked Rich, as he looked out of the window. Just then there was the sound of thunder, and the rain came down so hard that the plane rocked. Inside the plane, the air was hot and damp. Mark tried to look out of the window, but the rain was coming down so hard that he couldn't see anything. "Boy, is it ever hot!" said Rich.

"That's because we're so near the equator here," said Mark.

The pilot of the plane was standing beside the young men, smiling down at them. "You had better be prepared for heat and more heat if you're going up the Amazon," he said.

As the pilot spoke, the rain stopped as suddenly as it had started. Rich looked at the pilot in surprise. "It rains like that almost every day at just about this time," said the pilot. "When it does, you had better stay inside."

The young men looked out of the window. Rushing water covered the runway.

The sun came out, and the pilot opened the door of the plane. As the young men stepped out of the plane, they saw dozens of brown, smiling faces turned toward them. People were coming out of the airport building, and trucks were on the airport field.

The young men walked around puddles of water and headed toward the biggest building.

"I don't know what you think," said Rich, "but I think it's hot." He stopped to wipe his face with his handkerchief. "I don't think I've ever been this hot before!" he exclaimed, as he picked up his suitcase and followed Mark. (726)

Lucky Travelers

"Look at the size of that one!" said Mark, pointing to a big ship at the docks. The young men had walked down to the docks and were standing looking at the hundreds of ships and boats in the harbor.

All around them, men worked at loading and unloading the ships. There were ships from all over the world, and the men watched as the workers moved among them. There was coffee in great bags being loaded on one ship. Great piles of lumber had been unloaded from others. Everyone was busy, and now and then the young men moved to let a truck pass. They listened to the workers as they talked, but they couldn't understand much of what they heard. Then they noticed a man standing beside them. He was tall and slim, and he wore a blue coat with gold on the sleeves. He was watching the workers as they loaded the big ship that Mark had pointed out.

The stranger turned to Mark and Rich and said, "What are you fellows doing here? Are you going up the river?"

"You speak English!" said Mark.

The man smiled at them. "You two must be from the States," he said.

"Yes, we are," replied Rich.

"We would like to go up the river," said Mark. "Do you know anyone who could use two good workers?"

The man looked at Mark and Rich. Then he put out his hand. "I'm Captain Van Root," he said. "And that's my ship, the KATARINA. We've come from Holland. We're going up the river tomorrow as far as Manaus, if that will help you. But, what can you do? Can either one of you cook?"

"That's for me!" Rich exclaimed.

"You'd better watch him, sir," said Mark, laughing. "He'll eat everything he cooks."

Captain Van Root laughed. "There's plenty to eat," he said. "But I need a hand to work on the deck, too." He looked at Mark.

"I'll be glad to do that, sir," said Mark.

"Fine," said the Captain. "You have a ship!"

"When do we leave?" Mark asked.

"We're almost loaded now, but we won't leave until noon tomorrow. You had better be on board ship early in the morning, though," said the Captain.

The young men shook the Captain's hand and gave him their names. Then they walked down the docks and were soon out of sight. Captain Van Root stood watching them. He smiled. "Nice fellows," he said to himself. Then he moved toward the KATARINA.

Mark and Rich walked back toward their hotel, looking for a place to eat. The air was hot and damp.

"How about eating out-of-doors, Mark?" Rich asked. "I don't think I can stand the heat inside another building." They saw a place ahead and found a table under a tree. As they sat down, a small boy came up to them. He had several bottles in his hands and something wrapped in paper.

"Do you want to buy some giant ants? A big bug?" He was smiling as he held out first one bottle and then another to the men. Rich and Mark looked at the bottles closely. One bottle was filled with giant black ants, each one over an inch long. The other bottle contained a green and black beetle at least four inches long.

"That's the biggest beetle I ever saw!" exclaimed Mark. "But, no thanks, we don't want anything."

"How about a stuffed fish?" asked the little boy with an anxious smile.

"What kind of fish?" asked Rich.

"A piranha, sir!" said the little boy.

"A piranha!" exclaimed Mark. "Show it to us!"

The boy unwrapped something from the paper that he was carrying and placed it on the table. There, staring up at Mark and Rich, was the ugliest fish they had ever seen. It was only about ten inches long. Its mouth was open, showing dozens of teeth that looked like sharp needles.

"Where did you get it?" asked Mark.

"My father gets them from the fishermen far up the great river," answered the boy.

"Well, I'm sorry, but we really don't want to buy anything," said Mark.

The boy turned and walked sadly down the street.

"Mark, that's what we came here to get! Why didn't you buy it?" Rich asked.

"We came here to find live piranha, Rich. Just wait. We'll find them," said Mark.

The young men ate their meal and walked back to their hotel. They were very tired after the day's flight, so they went to bed early. Just before he went to sleep, Rich raised himself up on one elbow. He looked over at Mark and asked, "Do you really think we'll find the piranhas, Mark?"

"We'll find them, Rich. We're going to Manaus and we'll find them. Now go to sleep. We have to get up early to be on the ship." Mark turned over and was soon asleep.

Rich lay in the dark, looking out of the window at the shadows outside. He felt like pinching himself. It was hard to believe that it was just that morning that they had left their homes. Now they were in the heart of the tropics, on the banks of the mighty Amazon. It had been an exciting day. (881)

On the Amazon

"How's it going, Rich?" asked Mark.

"Fine, I guess," replied Rich, wearily. "It's awfully hot down there, though. I wish I had a job up here on deck. I'm so hot, I'm not even hungry."

The young men were standing at the rail of the KATARINA, leaning over and watching the thick jungle slip past. Night was coming very fast. Dark shadows reached across the water between the ship and the shore. Now and then a bright bird would flash out of the dark jungle and into the light. Then it would disappear again.

The men had awakened early that morning. They had reached the KATARINA just as the sun came up over the edge of the jungle. They had never seen so much excitement as there was around the ships! Dozens of small boats, each with a bright red or blue sail, worked their way out of the harbor and into the river. Several big ships were being loaded, and they noticed that other ships had come in during the night. They stood on the deck and looked around for Captain Van Root. He came out of his cabin and took the men on a complete tour of the ship. They met the men they would be working with on the trip up the river to Manaus.

Some of the men were young, no older than Rich and Mark. One young man had been very friendly. "I'm glad you're with us," he said. "I will see you later and we can talk."

Neither Mark nor Rich could believe his eyes when the ship pulled out into the Amazon. The water was very muddy, and there were boats and ships every-where. Within a few hours, theirs was the only ship in sight. The pilot kept the ship close to the bank of the river. The men could see the jungle, and some-times almost touch the branches of the trees and the vines that hung from the trees. Captain Van Root sent Rich below to the galley where he was to help the two ship's cooks prepare the meals. Mark stayed on deck. One of the men gave him a big brush and told him to get busy mopping the deck.

"I really didn't work very hard today," said Mark. "How about you?"

"I didn't have too much to do either," replied Rich. "Believe it or not, I've seen so much food today that I don't think I ever want to see more!"

"Oh, ho!" laughed Mark. "I'll believe that when I see it!"

Someone came through the darkness and stood beside them. It was the young man who had spoken to them that morning. He told them his name was Hans. Soon the three young men were talking like old friends. Hans told Mark and Rich that this was his ninth trip up the Amazon River. Rich and Mark stared at him in disbelief.

"You look too young!" said Mark.

"Well, I'm only twenty, but I've been with this ship since I was sixteen," explained Hans. Then he turned to them and asked, "Why are you two going up the river? What are you going to do in Manaus?"

"We want to see this part of the world," replied Rich, "and we want to find the piranha."

"The piranha! You want to find the piranha!" Hans stepped back and looked at Rich as if he could not believe what he had heard. "But why?" he asked.

"When we heard about the piranha, we volunteered to get one for a government aquarium," said Mark.

20

"Well, I've seen piranha fish. They're an ugly, awful type of fish," said Hans.

"Where? Where did you see them?" asked Rich.

"In a small river, off the Rio Negro, above Manaus," said Hans. "I was there to see a tribe of Indians. I did not know about the piranha then, but I soon learned about them."

"What happened? What did you see?" Mark asked.

"I will tell you," Hans replied. He leaned back against the rail and told his story. "I was visiting the Indians. It was about noon and we were eating. Suddenly, there was a great noise down along the river.

Everyone ran to see what the noise was. I could tell the Indians were frightened, but I didn't know why. When I reached the river, I saw many monkeys in a tree that hung out over the river. They were screaming and jumping up and down. There was blood on the water below them. One of the Indians told me that a monkey had fallen into the river and that the piranha fish had eaten him. I couldn't believe that, for there was nothing left of the monkey. As we stood there, the monkeys gave a loud scream. We looked up in time to see another monkey slip from the tree and fall into the river. In a second, those terrible fish were all around the monkey. In another second, there was no monkey. One of the Indians took a long pole and pulled out a skeleton. Every bit of flesh had been stripped from the monkey's bones in just a minute's time. It was an awful sight, and I have never forgotten it."

Mark and Rich shivered and looked at each other. Finally Mark asked, "Would they eat a man?"

"Yes, they would," Hans said, quietly. "There are thousands of the piranha fish in the river, and when blood is drawn, they all come with their sharp teeth. Men have died or have had the flesh stripped off their legs or arms by the piranhas. Do you still want to see them?"

"Yes!" said Mark. "I don't think I want to see the piranhas kill anything, but I don't want to go home without getting a real, live piranha. That's why we came here."

Rich nodded his head, agreeing with Mark. Hans shrugged his shoulders and looked out across the dark river. "Well, if you must get one, maybe my friend in Manaus will take us up the Rio Negro. But I wish you did not even want to see the piranha. It is a terrible, terrible fish!"

Other men had joined them on the deck. The ship moved quietly through the water. There was not a star in the sky, nor was there any moon. Only the lights of the ship, gleaming on the water, broke the darkness. The air was still warm, but the night was quiet and peaceful. Rich and Mark sat down together and listened as the men told of other nights on other rivers of the world.

Suddenly, Rich grabbed Mark by the arm. "Listen! Do you hear that?"

"Hear what?" several of the men asked.

"I hear a bell. There's a bell ringing somewhere. Don't you hear it?"

The men laughed. "That's a bird," one of them said. "Haven't you ever heard of the bellbird?"

"Oh, come on, now!" said Rich. "I do hear a bell. You hear it, don't you, Mark? Hans?"

"Yes, Rich, I hear it," answered Hans, softly. "And it is a bird. It's the bellbird. I have heard it many times on quiet nights like this. It always reminds me of a church bell ringing at home."

Everyone was quiet. They heard nothing except the sound of the great engines and the swishing of the water in the river. Then it came, "Dong, dong! Dong, dong! Dong, dong!"

"Don't you believe me, Rich?" asked Hans.

"Well. . .," answered Rich. He looked at Mark.

"It's true, Rich," said Mark, quietly. "I've read about the bellbird many times."

One by one the men stretched out on their mats on the deck. Mark and Rich unrolled their sleeping bags and lay down. As they fell asleep, they could hear, ringing across the water, "Dong, dong! Dong! dong! Dong, dong!" (1304)

A Shrunken Head

The next morning when Rich came up on deck from the galley, he found Mark standing at the rail, looking at the river. He wiped his face and walked over to Mark. "Boy, do you ever have it easy!" he said. "That galley is so hot I think I might bake!"

Captain Van Root was standing nearby. He smiled at Rich and said, "Why don't you take it easy for the rest of the day? You're not used to this heat, and we don't want to lose a good man. That goes for you too, Mark. You fellows enjoy the river. There really isn't much to do now."

Mark and Rich worked their way to the bow of the ship and stood there looking at the mighty Amazon. Sometimes the jungle was broken by wide meadows. Other times the ship was so close to the bank of the river that the men felt they could reach out and pick the brightly-colored flowers that hung from the trees. Birds of every color were flying in and out of the dense jungle. Once, a great macaw that was at least three feet long swooped low over the bow. Both Rich and Mark reached for the bird. They heard laughter behind them and turned around. Hans was standing there watching them.

"You'll never catch him!" said Hans. "I've tried many times, but they're wise old birds."

Now and then they saw small villages with houses built of palm leaves and poles. All of the houses were built on poles above the ground. Hans explained that during the rainy season the Amazon was sometimes two hundred miles wide, and the houses had to be high above the ground.

There were small boats everywhere. There were no roads in this part of the country, and no bridges across the Amazon. Men, women, and children rowed boats and waved at the ship as it passed. Some of the boats had covers over them to protect the people from the sun and rain. Many of the boats were canoes cut from logs or made of bark. One boat came very near the ship. Mark noticed something in the boat. "I wonder what they're carrying," he said. "It looks like pieces of wood. What do you suppose they do with them?"

Captain Van Root was standing near the men again, and he answered Mark. "Those are pieces of the timbo vine. The Indians use them to make a poison for killing fish."

Mark and Rich looked so curious that Captain Van Root continued. "The Indians cut those pieces of the timbo vine. They take them back to their village. The women and children beat the vine until it is broken into strings. The vine contains a poison. The Indians make nets and set them in the river. Everyone gets in the river and makes a lot of noise to drive the fish toward the nets. When there are many fish in the net, the men enter the water and drag the timbo vine through the water. The poison in the vine then kills the fish."

"Doesn't the poison kill the Indians, too?" Mark asked the Captain.

"No, it doesn't. No one has ever heard of an Indian being killed by the timbo poison, but many fish are killed by it," said the Captain. "Look there!" The Captain pointed up the river to a big island.

"That's a floating island," he said. "You've seen hundreds of them moving down the river by now."

"But there's a village on that island," said Rich. "What a way to live!"

"Those floating islands are safer than the jungle, Rich," replied the Captain. "The Indians will live on the island until the rainy season comes. Then they'll move their village back to the jungle."

"Just imagine having your own island, and a floating one at that!" said Mark. Both he and Rich watched the island until it was out of sight.

Eisenhower School
Norton, Kansas

That afternoon most of the men sat in the shade on the deck. They would be in Manaus the next day, but there was little work that had to be done now. One of the men was old, with white hair and bright blue eyes. He was holding something, turning it over and over in his hands. Mark moved over to where the old man was sitting.

"What is it you have there?" Mark asked.

"It's a shrunken head," said the old man. "Here, do you want to hold it?" He held the head out for Mark to take.

Mark jumped back and shook his head. "No, no thanks," he said. "Where did you get it?"

"Oh, I got it from an Indian up the Rio Negro," said the old man. "He wanted a watch I had, and I wanted this man's head. So, we made a trade."

"Do you mean that thing was once the head of a man?" Mark asked.

"It sure was. This was the grandfather of the man who traded with me." The old man turned the head over slowly in his hands and smiled at it.

"How did he make it that size?" asked Rich, joining Mark and the old man.

"I don't know," answered the old man. "Some say the Indians use the leaves and roots of plants. Others say they use hot sand. But I'm not sure."

"Where do they get the heads? Are there many of them? Can anyone trade for them?" Rich asked.

The old man smiled at Rich. "One question at a time, young man. In some Indian tribes, everyone shrinks the heads of his parents when the parents die. Others go head hunting and take the heads of their enemies. The Indian that I got this one from had about a dozen other shrunken heads. I wouldn't try to trade for them, if I were you. I got this head a long time ago. This little fellow and I have become quite good friends." The old man touched the head very gently.

(1005)

Manaus

The big ship pulled alongside the pier. Mark and Rich were standing at the rail, looking at the city of Manaus. The day was clear, and white clouds floated high above the city. On the docks, hundreds of people waited to greet the ship. The harbor, like the one at Belem, was filled with small boats. However, there were only three other big ships at the docks in Manaus when the KATARINA arrived. Small boats darted this way and that. The Indians and the people of Manaus were here to do their marketing and to bring goods to sell at the market.

"It's almost like a fair," said Mark, as he looked at the people and the boats. "Did you ever see so much color in one place?"

Captain Van Root spoke to the young men. "You fellows have five days here before we return to Belem. Have a good time and stay out of trouble." He gave each of them a friendly pat on the back and went down the ship's gangplank.

"Let's go!" said Rich. He started to follow the Captain down the gangplank.

"Wait for me!" It was Hans, their young friend, calling. He was carrying a big box on his shoulder.

"What do you have there?" asked Mark.

"Gifts for my Indian friends," smiled Hans. "Didn't you say you wanted to visit a native village?" He set the big box down and wiped his wet face. "I guess you know by now that it isn't any cooler in Manaus than it was in Belem!"

The young men picked up their bags and walked down the gangplank. They worked their way through the crowd of people standing around on the dock. Everyone greeted them and smiled at them. One little boy came up to them with bottles in his hands. "Want some giant ants? Want a big bug?"

"Not again!" said Rich, but he stopped and looked closely at the bottles. "Hans," he said, "do you think we'll find ants like these when we go to visit the Indian village?"

"No," replied Hans, "you will not. Those giant ants are rare. If you want some, you had better buy them now from the boy."

The little boy beamed. He held out a bottle that had six large black ants in it. Soon Rich was carrying the bottle, and the little boy was smiling as he counted his money. Rich looked at his purchase. The ants were still alive. When they stretched their legs, they were two inches long. Suddenly, Rich stopped and exclaimed, "Say, there's a red ant with wings in this bottle!"

"That is a male ant," said Hans. "You really have a prize there. They are very hard to find."

"Do you think the ants will live?" Rich asked Hans, quite anxiously.

"If you feed them well, yes," replied Hans.

In a few minutes they came to a small hotel. The man at the desk smiled and spoke to them.

"What's he saying?" Rich asked Hans.

"He said that he has a room for three tired young men," replied Hans.

"Say, do you speak Portuguese?" asked Mark.

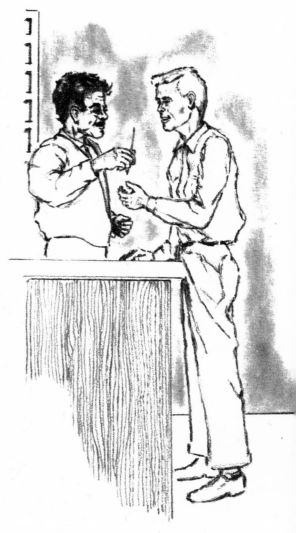

"Yes, I speak enough to understand what people are saying to me and I can make them understand me," said Hans. "When you work in a country as long as I have, you must learn some of the language. There are a number of languages spoken in Brazil, but almost everyone understands Portuguese."

Their room was hot, so the men quickly unpacked their bags and went out on the street again. There were open markets everywhere they looked. In one market they saw large pieces of meat hanging. There was the head of a sheep on a tray.

"What do you do with that?" asked Rich.

"Many people like it very much, young man," said the man in the market. "It is very good to eat."

"You may have noticed that all the meat is fresh," said Hans. "There is no ice here, and no way to keep meat longer than for a day or two. So, all meat must be freshly killed."

Rich and Mark turned away. "You know," said Rich, "I don't feel very hungry right now." Mark nodded his head. Hans and the man in the market laughed at the young men.

In the center of the city they saw a beautiful building. It stood alone, surrounded by big trees and courtyards. "This is the Opera House," said Hans. "It is one of the finest buildings in all South America."

"Is it used often?" asked Mark.

"No," replied Hans. "The building is not used very much. Although it was built many years ago, you can see that the people have kept it in good shape. They are very proud of this Opera House. Would you like to go in?"

The three friends walked through the Opera House. Great colored paintings covered the walls, and the floors were made of brightly-colored tiles. It was quiet and cool inside.

"Imagine finding a building like this in the heart of the jungle!" exclaimed Mark. He reached out and touched the gold on one of the walls.

"Anywhere you go in the world," said Hans, quietly, "you will find that people admire beautiful things. They will give their money and their time to build something that will always remind them of beauty."

As they walked out of the Opera House, Hans said, "I must go to see my friend now. I will meet you after dinner. I may have good news for you then." With that, he turned and walked away among the crowds of people on the street.

Later that night, when the streets were quiet and Mark and Rich were sitting on the steps in front of the hotel, Hans returned. "Well, friends, I have good news," he said, smiling.

"What is it?" asked Rich.

"Tomorrow we go up the Rio Negro," said Hans. "My friend will take us to the Indian village."

Both Mark and Rich started to ask questions, but Hans just laughed and said, "Tomorrow I will answer all of your questions. Tonight we must get some sleep. The trip up the Rio Negro will be a long, hard one. Let's go to bed."

The three men climbed the stairs to their room. It was still very hot. The room was dark. Rich felt the wall beside the door. "Where's the light switch?" he asked.

Hans laughed. "I'm afraid you won't find a light switch in this hotel," he replied. "There is not much electricity in Manaus." He struck a match and moved to a table. As he lit an oil lamp, he said, "Here's your electric light, Rich!"

(1117)

Up the Rio Negro

The little boat had been chugging along for what seemed like hours to Rich and Mark. The sun was high in the sky and it was very hot. Mark and Rich were sitting in the shade of a palm-leaf cover that was built over the boat. Hans sat in the bow of the boat. Now and then Hans would say a word or two to Andy, the young man who was steering. Andy sat quietly, watching both banks of the river and steering the boat with great skill.

The Rio Negro was a slow-moving river that was just as muddy as the Amazon. Andy did not allow the boat to move far from the bank of the river, so every now and then, Hans had to reach up and brush the vines aside so that the little boat could move through safely. Often a bright orange or blue bird would flash by their boat. Huge butterflies, bright as the rainbow fluttered near them.

Hans sat up quickly and cried, "Watch out, Andy!" He pointed to something ahead of them. Andy's smile disappeared, and he quickly steered the boat toward the middle of the river. Mark and Rich knew something was wrong. Just then they saw it—a snake so big they could not believe their eyes. It was hanging from a tree that leaned far out over the water.

When the snake saw the boat, it moved slowly downward and dropped into the river. It was at least thirty feet long, and as it swam, its great head moved from side to side. It was so close that the men could see its beady black eyes. Suddenly, it disappeared under the water.

Hans whistled. "Anaconda!" he said.

"What if we hadn't seen it first?" Rich asked. He shivered and moved closer to Mark.

"The anaconda will usually not hurt you," said Andy. "But if we had run into it with the boat, it could have been very unpleasant."

For the next few miles, the men sat up and looked closely at every tree that hung out over the river. Once or twice they saw what they thought was another anaconda, but it was just a thick vine. Soon Hans called to Andy and pointed off to the right where a small stream flowed into the river. Andy nodded his head and steered the boat slowly into the stream. The trees and vines were so thick on either side of the stream that the men could not see beyond them. Every so often all of them had to duck down as they passed under a low-hanging tree. Once a tangle of vines caught the palm-leaf cover of the boat and pulled it into the stream.

The boat began moving slower and slower. Mark and Rich knew something was about to happen since Andy and Hans were both looking closely ahead. Then the motor of the boat grew silent, and they drifted against the bank. Hans jumped from the boat and pulled the boat up on the bank. "Come on, fellows!" he said. "Here's where we start walking."

A path from the bank led into the jungle. Mark and Rich helped Andy and Hans as they tied the boat to a tree and then lifted Hans' big box from the boat. Hans swung the box up on his shoulder and started up the path. Andy followed Hans, with Rich and Mark close behind.

There was little sunlight in the deep jungle. The men could hear all kinds of noises in the underbrush along the path and in the trees overhead.

The heat was almost more than the men could bear. "How much farther do we have to go?" asked Rich, as he wiped his face on his sleeve. "Boy, I've never been this hot before."

"It's not much farther now," replied Hans.

In a few minutes, Hans turned left on another path. After walking about one hundred yards, he stopped, set his box down, and turned to the men behind him. "Here we are!" he said.

The three young men moved quickly to Hans' side. They looked ahead anxiously. There was a clearing in the jungle, not more than fifty feet wide. A house made of poles and of palm and banana tree leaves stood in the clearing. Hans cupped his hands to his mouth and shouted, "Hello, Watabi!"

Suddenly, there were several little people where there had been no one a moment before. None of the people was over five feet tall. They wore no clothes, and their long black hair hung to their shoulders. There were women and small children and more than a dozen men. One man stepped forward, his face beaming. His face was as brown as the bark of a tree, and his white teeth gleamed as he smiled at Hans. Hans stepped forward to meet him, and the two men shook hands. Then Hans turned to the other men behind him.

"This is my friend Watabi," Hans said to the young men. "And these are my friends Mark and Rich and Andy," he told Watabi.

The old man looked at the strangers carefully. Then he shook hands with them and said, "You are most welcome, if you are friends of my friend Hans."

Rich hit Mark with his elbow. "Why he speaks English!" Rich said with surprise.

Watabi smiled. "Yes, my young friend, I do speak English. Many years ago, an American man-of-God lived with my people. He taught us to speak his tongue, and we have taught it to our children. Come, you must see our home." He led the way toward the big house.

There was one door leading into the house. As the men stepped through the door, they found it was so dark inside that they could not see. As their eyes became used to the darkness, they saw that the house was one large room. In the center of the room was a circle of stones where a fire had been burning. Around the walls there were several hammocks swung between tree trunks. The hammocks were woven of vines and leaves of the palm tree. "Our home is very simple as you can see. You will stay the night, won't you?" asked Watabi.

"Yes, we can stay the night," said Hans.

46

"Then we must build a house," said Watabi. He turned to his people and spoke to them rapidly in his own language. Then the Indians left.

"Build us a house?" said Mark. "Hans, tell them they don't have to do that. We can sleep outside, or we can sleep here on the floor."

Hans laughed. "You just watch them, Mark. They would not be happy if they could not build a house for us. Besides, you would not want to sleep outside or on the floor. You don't realize what kinds of things crawl around in this jungle at night!"

The men stepped outside. All of the Indians had gone into the jungle and were just coming back. They chose a circle of trees in the clearing. Some of them tied poles between the trees with vines that they had cut. When the poles were in place, others brought leaves from banana trees and tied them to the poles. In a few minute's time, there was a snug little house, just like the big house in the center of the clearing. Then the Indian women came with the hammocks. They tied them to the tree trunks in the little house. Each of the men then had a bed.

Rich was so pleased that he moved over to one of the hammocks and said, "Man, sleeping in this is going to be great!" He swung his leg up and raised himself into the hammock.

Before Rich knew what was happening, he was lying on his face on the dirt floor. Everyone laughed as he picked himself up. Hans was laughing harder than the rest. "There's a trick to getting into one of those hammocks, Rich," he said. "And there's also a trick to staying in one." He moved quickly and then was in the hammock, swinging back and forth.

"I guess I've got some learning to do," Rich said, his face a bright red.

As the men sat talking with Watabi and the other men of the Indian tribe, the women built a fire outside the big house and began preparing the meal. Everyone seemed to have a job to do. Some of the children carried water to their mothers. Others brought green bananas and other fruit. Rich's nose began to twitch. "Um-m-m! What is that?" he asked, as he sniffed the air.

Watabi smiled at him. "Tonight we will have a feast in honor of my new friends. Wait. It is to be a big surprise for you!"

Just when Mark and Rich thought they could stand their hunger no longer, one of the women came to the circle of men and said to Watabi, "We are ready." Old Watabi got to his feet. The men followed him to the big house. A fire had been built in the circle of stones, and the men sat down around the fire. The four guests were seated beside Watabi. Then came the women, carrying the food on banana leaves.

Rich could hardly believe his eyes when he saw what one of the women carried. It was a pig, roasted whole. It smelled wonderful. The women sat down. The children sat quietly behind them. Watabi picked up a knife and cut the pig into pieces. He gave some to each of his guests and some to each member of the tribe. Then he smiled and said, "We will eat."

Watabi picked the meat up in his fingers and bit into it. Rich looked around at the Indians. All the Indians were eating, Andy and Hans were eating, but he and Mark were both still waiting.

Finally, Hans leaned over and whispered to Rich, "Eat with your fingers. There are no knives and forks here in the jungle."

There were sweet potatoes and tender white fish that had been roasted in the coals of the fire. There were small, flat cakes made of casava flour, and the honey from wild bees. The men ate as if they had never eaten before. When they finished, Watabi placed more food before them.

At a signal from Watabi, one of the women left the circle and went outside. When she returned, she carried a large bowl which she set before Watabi. The old man turned to his guests. "Now you must have the best of our food," he said. With a big spoon, he reached into the bowl and began giving everyone some of the food. Rich and Mark looked at the food curiously. "These are roasted green bananas," said Watabi. "They were roasted in wild honey."

Later, when the women had cleared away the food and the banana leaves, Hans got up and went outside. Soon he returned, carrying his big box. All of the children gathered around. The parents were just as anxious as the children to see what the box held. Hans opened the lid carefully. Screams of delight came from all the people. There were bright red and blue beads and rings, and shiny knives and spoons for the children and the women. For the men, there were two axes, some hunting knives, and—best of all—pipes for their tobacco!

Hans had saved one gift for the very last. He had set it aside carefully. At last he took out a small box and handed it to old Watabi. The old chief looked at the box. He held it in his hands and touched it softly. Then he opened it. When he looked up, there were tears in his eyes. He passed the box around for everyone to see. A watch was in the box, a shiny, ticking watch on a chain. Watabi lifted the watch from the box and put the chain around his neck. The watch hung on his bare chest, and in the firelight, it gleamed almost as brightly as Watabi's face.

(2033)

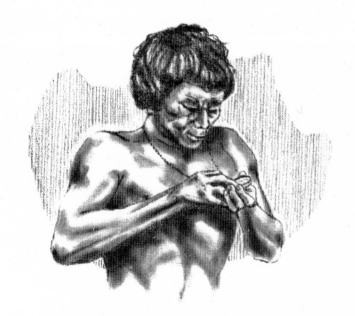

Piranha!

Birds sang, pigs grunted, and children laughed. Mark opened his eyes and saw that the sun was up. He moved carefully in his hammock and looked at the other hammocks. Hans and Andy were already up and gone, but Rich was still asleep. Mark lay quietly for a few minutes, listening to the sounds of the village awakening. He could hear the men and women talking quietly. Now and then there was the chatter of monkeys or the screech of a macaw. He called to Rich, but Rich didn't move. Finally, Mark swung carefully out of his hammock and moved over to Rich's hammock. He shook his sleeping friend.

"Come on, Rich," he said. "Time to get up!"

Rich sat up suddenly, and the hammock swung to one side. Rich lay in the dirt again.

Rich had a foolish grin on his face when he and Mark came out of the house. "Some day," he said, "I'll learn to ride one of those things!"

Mark and Rich could feel the excitement in the air. Hans and Andy were gone, and many of the men had gone with them. Watabi greeted his guests and led them over to a fire for their breakfast. They ate quickly, and then Watabi stood up and said, "I understand you want to go fishing."

"Fishing!" exclaimed Mark. "Who said we wanted to go fishing?"

Watabi smiled. "Someone told me you wanted to catch a very special fish. A piranha perhaps?"

"Piranha!" said Rich. "Do you mean. . .?"

"Today you will get your piranha," said Watabi. "Come, the men are waiting for us." He stepped quickly toward a path leading into the jungle. Rich and Mark followed him. Soon they came to another clearing where they found the men of the tribe, Andy and Hans, and several head of cattle. The cattle were moving around and around. When the men saw Watabi, they stood waiting for him to speak.

"Today we will move the cattle to the other side of the stream," Watabi said to the men. "We must take them to market."

The men nodded and started moving the cattle out of the clearing. The young men followed, walking with Watabi. As they walked, Watabi spoke of the trip ahead. "Each year we must take our cattle to market. We must drive them many miles to market to trade them for things we need. To get to market, we must cross the stream. If we are not careful, the piranha will kill our cattle."

"Do you mean the piranha could eat a whole cow?" asked Rich.

"Yes," said Watabi. "The piranha work together. Not even a cow can last when the piranha are hungry."

They had reached the bank of the stream. Then the men separated the cattle, leaving one old cow behind. They drove the others up the stream and waited. Two men stood by the old cow. Suddenly, everyone was quiet.

"Do you have the net?" asked Watabi. An Indian standing near him nodded his head and showed the net he had to Watabi. The net was tied on the end of a long pole.

"What are they going to do?" asked Mark. His voice was almost a whisper.

"You may not like this," replied Hans, "but they must do it." He looked worried and a little sad.

Everyone looked at Watabi. The men up the stream with the cattle did not move. They were watching their chief. Watabi slowly raised his arm, and one of the two men standing beside him stepped forward and moved the old cow to the edge of the stream. He held a long knife in his hand. Watabi shouted, "Now!" and the knife flashed.

The knife cut the throat of the old cow. As the cut was made, Watabi and the two Indians pushed the cow into the stream. Suddenly, there was movement in the water, and hundreds of small fish were there, fighting each other and striking the cow. Hundreds more of the fish came. Blood flowed on the surface of the stream. The cow had disappeared.

Mark and Rich turned away, their faces white. As they turned, they saw Hans with his back turned to the stream.

"Why did you do it? Why?" asked Rich looking at old Watabi.

Old Watabi put his hand on Rich's shoulder and answered quietly. "Look up the stream, my son. See, the other cattle have already swum across. We had to kill the old cow. Each time we cross this stream with our cattle, we must kill one cow."

"Why?" Rich asked again.

"The piranha would kill all our cattle if we did not lead them away as we did just now," said Watabi. "I know it seems cruel, but this is the way we must live with the awful piranha."

"Why did the fish come so quickly?" asked Mark.

"The piranha come whenever there is blood," said Watabi. "We drew blood from the old cow knowing  that all the piranha anywhere around here would come at once. You saw how quickly they came. Remember, I had my men to protect, too. They had to cross the stream and drive the cattle. If we had not killed the cow as we did, the piranha would have killed my men as well as the cattle."

Watabi turned away slowly. The four young men and the two Indians followed him as he led the way back to the house in the clearing.

When they reached the big house, Watabi turned to one of his men and said, "Do you have them?"

The Indian nodded and put the fishing net in front of Watabi. Mark and Rich looked down and gasped. There in the net were two piranhas, fighting for their lives. Their teeth were snapping, and they were gasping for air.

Watabi turned to the young men. "I believe you wanted these, didn't you?" (983)

Back to Manaus

"You must come to see my people again," said old Watabi. He was standing beside the stream, watching his guests as they loaded their boat and prepared to return to Manaus. Behind him were the women, the children, and two men of the tribe. The other men were still away, driving the cattle to the market.

Just before Hans pushed off, one of the Indian men came forward, holding something in his hands. Old Watabi took the object from the man and spoke to Mark and Rich. "I have a gift for you, my young friends. This is what you came to my village in search of. Take them back to your people. Let your people see them and know about them." He lifted the covering over the object. It was a glass tank with the two piranhas in it!

"My men have prepared the fish for you so that you may return to your own country safely with them," Watabi continued. "The tank is very strong. The fish will live, but they will not be able to escape from the tank."

Both Mark and Rich smiled at Watabi. "We will never forget these days we have spent with you and your people. It has been an experience that we will remember always," said Mark.

The young men thanked Watabi and took his gift. Hans jumped into the boat, and the two Indian men gave it a mighty shove. The boat swung into the river, and Andy started the motor. Mark and Rich looked back. Watabi, the women and children, and the two Indian men were standing as they had left them. The young men waved until they had rounded a bend in the stream and could no longer see the friendly Indians.

"This is one trip I'll never forget," said Mark. Turning to Hans he added, "Thank you, Hans, for taking us. I'm sorry if we acted as if we didn't enjoy it. We did. It will be something to remember always."

The little boat chugged quietly ahead. Rich rested his head on his arms and slept. Hans and Mark talked quietly, watching the banks of the stream as they passed along.

"Flop!" Something dropped from a high tree and hit the water. The noise was loud enough to awaken Rich. He sat up and looked around.

"What was that?" asked Mark.

Andy stopped the motor and the boat drifted along silently. They all looked toward the place from which the noise had come. Suddenly, they saw something swimming in the water.

"Why, it's a bird!" said Hans.

"Hoatzin!" cried Andy. He pointed to the tree from which the bird had come. "It's a baby hoatzin!"

"What's a hoatzin?" asked Rich. The bird had disappeared in a tangle of vines in the stream.

"The hoatzin is one of the oddest birds in the world," Andy answered. "No one has ever been able to keep it alive in a zoo. The hoatzin lives in this part of South America. No one knows why it can live only here and nowhere else."

Andy had steered the
boat to the bank under the
big tree. He looked all
around. "There's one now!"
he cried.

There, sitting high in the branches of the tree, was
an odd looking bird, almost two feet long. It had a
tuft of feathers on its head, big claws, and bright red
eyes. The skin around its eyes was blue. It looked
at the men for a minute. Then it spread its wings and
tried to fly away. It flopped its wings, squawked, and
landed clumsily in the bushes across the stream. The
men laughed. They had never seen such a silly looking bird.

"Is there something wrong with the bird?" asked Hans. "It doesn't seem to be able to fly well."

"It has such funny feathers that it can't fly well," answered Andy. "But it can swim. When you frighten the young birds, they drop into the water and swim away. The nest of the hoatzin is always built in a tree over the water."

"Why can't they be kept alive when they're taken away from here?" asked Mark.

"No one knows for sure. But many people believe there is something in the food they eat that they cannot get when they're taken out of the jungle. The hoatzin eats only seeds, leaves, and buds of trees. It does not eat fish or insects or fruit. It likes the leaf of the mukkamukka plant best of all. I have seen the hoatzin tear a mukkamukka plant apart with its beak and its claws."

"I wish we could find just one to take back with us," said Rich.

"Ha!" laughed Mark. "You already have giant ants and the piranhas. I can just see you feeding a hoatzin, too!"

Andy started the motor and the boat swung out into the stream again. The sun was high in the sky, and the men could feel the heat. In a short time, they reached the Rio Negro and headed toward Manaus. Each of the men sat quietly, thinking his own thoughts of the events of the past days.

Pulling into Manaus, the first thing the men saw was the KATARINA, the only big ship at the docks. Andy steered the boat along the pier and the men jumped out. With a wave of his arm and a bright smile, Andy was gone.

"Well, have you young fellows been keeping out of trouble?" It was Captain Van Root speaking. He was leaning over the rail of the KATARINA, smiling down at them. "What did you bring with you?"

Mark and Hans and Rich looked at each other. Mark was holding the container that held the two piranhas. No one said anything. Watabi and the friendly Indians; the old cow and the bloody stream; the deadly snapping fish; all were too fresh in their memories. Maybe sometime on the trip back to Belem they could tell Captain Van Root about their trip up the Rio Negro, but not today.

They walked wearily up the gangplank, and with a smile at the Captain, the three friends headed for a shady spot on the deck.

Glossary

The following system of indicating pronunciation is used by permission of the publishers of Webster's New International Dictionary, Second Edition, copyright, 1934, 1939, 1945, 1950, 1953, by G. & C. Merriam Co.

ā as in āle   ē as in ēve   ô as in ôbey

â as in câre   ê as in êvent   ô as in lôrd

å as in chåotic   ĕ as in ĕnd   ŏ as in ŏdd

ă as in ădd   ĕ as in silĕnt   oi as in oil

ă as in ăccount   ē as in makēr   ōō as in fōōd

ä as in ärm   ī as in īce   û as in ûnite

à as in àsk   ĭ as in ĭll   ŭ as in ŭp

á as in sofá   ō as in ōld   ŭ as in circŭs

Amazon (ăm'á zŏn). The world's largest river, located in South America. 7

anaconda (ăn'á kŏn'dà). A large South American snake that crushes its victim. 41

Belem (bĕ lĕm'). A port city in Brazil. 6

bellbird (bĕl'bûrd). A bird that makes a sound like a bell. 25

Brazil (brá zĭl'). A country in South America. 8

equator (ē kwā'tēr). A line half way between the North and South poles. 9

galley (găl'ĭ). The kitchen in a ship. 19

gangplank (găng'plăngk'). A long and narrow movable bridge used for entering or leaving a ship. 33

hammock (hăm'ŭk). A swinging bed that is attached to supports by cords at each end. 46

hoatzin (hō ăt'sĭn). A South American bird with olive-colored feathers. 62

Holland (hŏl'ănd). Another name for the Netherlands, a country in northern Europe. 13

macaw (mà kô'). A Central and South American parrot with very bright feathers. 27

Manaus (mà nous'). A city in Brazil. 13

piranha (pĭ rän'yà). A South American fish that is able to eat men and animals. 17

Portuguese (pōr'tū gēz). The language of Brazil. 35

Rio Negro (rē'ō nā'grō). A South American river. 21

tropics (trŏp'ĭcs). An area with a hot, wet climate. 17

* The number in parentheses on the last page of each chapter indicates the total number of words in that chapter. The number underlined on the last page of the story indicates the total number of words in the entire story.

Reading Maps

Mark and Rich sat in their room in Belem and looked at a map of South America. "I wonder how far it is to Manaus from here," said Mark.

Rich looked at the scale of miles. "I'd guess it's about a thousand miles," he said.

Mark shook his head. "That can't be right. I'd say it's more like six or seven hundred miles." Using a small ruler, he measured the distance from Belem to Manaus. Then he checked that distance against the scale of miles. "We're both wrong!" he said. "It's just eight hundred miles to Manaus."

Later, as the men returned to Belem from their trip up the Amazon, they looked at the map again. "Let's see if we can trace our trip," said Mark.

"We flew southeast from Florida to Belem," said Rich. "Here's Belem, about a hundred miles south of the equator. We went west up the Amazon River to Manaus, northwest up the Rio Negro, and then almost north to Watabi's village."

"I'd always thought that Belem was on the eastern coast of Brazil," said Mark. "Look here. The mouths of the Amazon are actually in the north central part of the country. Some of the rivers even flow north into the Amazon!"

News Story

Fish Caught Was Not Piranha, As Feared

DPI—For a short time yesterday, Fish and Game authorities in this area reacted with fear to a report that a fisherman had caught a deadly piranha fish in the Sacramento River.

A fisherman reported that a deadly piranha fish, one of the world's most vicious cannibals, had been caught in the Sacramento River. Authorities believed for a short while that their worst fears had been realized.

The piranha is a small South American fish found mainly in the Amazon River. Moving in schools of one hundred or more, piranhas have been known to strip the flesh from large animals and humans in just a few minutes' time.

Fish and Game authorities have restricted bringing the piranha into this country. Only a few aquariums have been allowed to display them. If the piranha were ever to get into the warm water of this country's western and southern rivers, there would be no way to control them.

The fish taken from the Sacramento River yesterday was not a piranha, but a member of the gar family. The excited fisherman was embarrassed, but Fish and Game authorities are breathing easily once again.

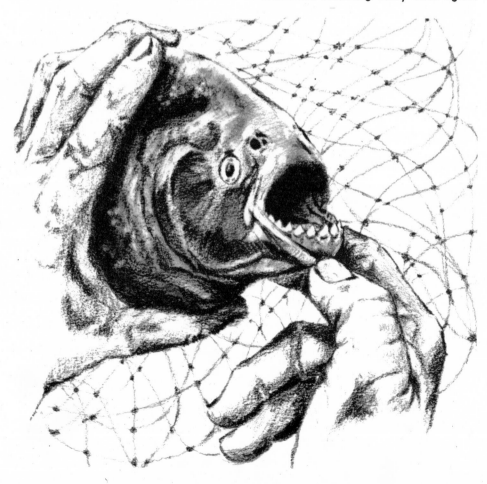

Tall Tales

Along the Amazon, everyone fears the anaconda. The people who live in that part of Brazil tell many stories about this great snake. They tell the stories to their children to teach them to beware of the great, giant anaconda.

Many years ago, when Belem was only a village on the Amazon, there was one anaconda that was known as the "King of the Amazon." He was so large that when he moved into the river, the water flowed over the banks and flooded the country. Someone said that his body was three miles long and a hundred feet wide. Villages were flattened whenever he moved over the land. All the people ran in terror from him.

Finally, men came with ships and cannons. When they learned of the giant anaconda, they went out to kill him. The old anaconda slipped under two of the ships and turned them upside down. Then many more ships were brought to the Amazon. One day the old anaconda was trapped between the village of Belem and the ocean. All day and all night he moved up and down the river. Each time he came near the ships, cannons were fired at him. Many times he opened his mouth and caught the cannon balls, but his blood flowed red on the Amazon.

Then came a night when the anaconda was hungry. He moved slowly toward the ocean. The men on the ships watched as the great snake plowed across the land, digging a great river as he moved. When he reached the ocean, he turned back because he could not live in the salt water of the ocean. As he moved back, he plowed another river. He went back and forth, back and forth from the village to the ocean. When morning came, there were more than a dozen great rivers flowing into the ocean, and the Amazon now had many mouths. The old anaconda was gone.

No one ever saw the old giant again, but one day men noticed that there was something rising above the land that they had not seen before. A great hole beside the Amazon seemed to lead under the land. The anaconda, old and tired and wounded, had pushed his great body deeper and deeper into the earth. High hills had risen to mark the grave of the great "King of the Amazon."

Eisenhower School
Norton, Kansas